ASIAPAC COMIC SERIES

The Chinese Code of Success

Maxims by Zhu Zi

Illustrated by Fu Chunjiang   Translated by Wu Jingyu

P9-DGO-661

ASIAPAC • SINGAPORE

Publisher
ASIAPAC BOOKS PTE LTD
996 Bendemeer Road #06-08/09
Kallang Basin Industrial Estate
Singapore 339944
Tel: (65) 392 8455
Fax: (65) 392 6455
Email apacbks@singnet.com.sg

Visit us at our Internet home page
www.asiapacbooks.com

First published January 1998

© 1998 ASIAPAC BOOKS, SINGAPORE
ISBN 981-3068-97-3

Cover design by TAP Design Pte Ltd
Body text in Helvetica 8/9pt
Printed in Singapore by Kin Keong Printing Co. Pte. Ltd

Publisher's Note

As a publisher dedicated to the promotion of works on Chinese culture and philosophy, we are pleased to bring you this graphic presentation of *The Chinese Code of Success: Maxims by Zhu Zi.*

Throughout Chinese history, there have been many teachings on regulating self and the family. Yet it is *Maxims by Zhu Zi* that has been chosen for inclusion in the Chinese Almanac, a book familiar to the traditional Chinese household. Since its writing more than three hundred years ago, it has been read and applied by many Chinese who find in it a practical formula for success in personal, family and social life.

In *The Chinese Code of Success*, you will find that many of the teachings are Confucianist in outlook — Zhu Zi has expressed lucidly the relationship between the individual, the family and society. This book will prove to be most relevant to today's materialistic society, where many individuals are using all means, sometimes unethical ones, to attain their goals for fame, power and wealth. Readers can discover for themselves how despite technological advancements, certain basic human values are always relevant for personal effectiveness.

We would like to take this opportunity to express our gratitude to Mr. Fu Chunjiang for his lively illustrations, and Professor Wu Jingyu for her translation and introduction. Our thanks, too, to the production team for putting in their best effort in the publication of this book.

Introduction

The original text of the maxims illustrated in this book is a tract of around 500 Chinese characters. That such a short article could make its author a household name in China and many sentences out of it have become maxims guiding the conduct of generations of Chinese is an extraordinary cultural phenomenon.

Besides the fact that he is the author of the tract on how to guide oneself and one's family and another book of notes on Confucian classics *Da Xue*《大学》and *Zhong Yong*《中庸》, not much is known about Zhu Bolu 朱伯庐 (1617 - 1688). He was a scholar born in the last years of the Ming Dynasty (1368 - 1644). All his life he never worked as an official, which was the occupation pursued by most educated men of his time. Instead, he devoted his life to the study and propagation of Confucianist ideas about moral perfection.

Chinese philosophers dating back to 770 BC have attached great importance to the moral cultivation of the individual. Though the founders of various schools of thought differ in their views on specific aspects of human life, they all shared the belief that the virtue of men is the basis of a good society. Therefore, the moral perfection of man, be him a king or an ordinary workman, has always been the primary concern of great Chinese thinkers, whose teachings have formed the Chinese cultural tradition.

The core of Chinese moral ideal is benevolence 仁 (*ren*). The definition of *ren*, given by Confucius, is "love for man", which means filial piety to one's parents, fraternal love for one's kinsfolk, kindheartedness towards others regardless of their social position and relationship to oneself, etc. "Love for man" also includes self-respect. The idea of *ren* is embodied in Zhu Bolu's teachings about how one should treat one's ancestors, parents, brothers and relatives, neighbours, traders, and other people one comes in contact with. And, as he sees it, a person's self-respect is demonstrated in his integrity, prudence, honesty, modesty and thriftiness. These fine qualities had been discussed by many great thinkers before him. One of the reasons why Zhu Bolu's writing has such widespread influence among the Chinese people is that he relates the profound ideas to the daily life of the ordinary people and expresses them in plain language that even people with little schooling can understand.

Times change, so do people's ideas about success and how to conduct themselves in life. However, there are certain basic moral principles universally honoured by people of different times and nations. Many of the teachings of Zhu Bolu fall into this category. That is why these maxims have such lasting value.

Needless to say, Zhu's views also have their limitations. It was impossible for him to look at social life beyond the pattern of human relationship existing at his time, or to see the relationship between man and nature beyond the level of scientific knowledge achieved then. Today, when we introduce the maxims by Zhu Zi, we do not expect readers to abide by them to the letter. What we hope is that readers will appreciate the essence of his teachings and find it helpful in their own pursuit for success and self-improvement.

Professor Wu Jingyu
Beijing

About the Illustrator

Fu Chunjiang, born in 1974, is a native of Chongqing municipality in southeastern China's Sichuan province. He has been fond of drawing ever since childhood and graduated in Chinese language studies. Fu loves traditional Chinese culture and has tried his hand at drawing comics. Since 1994 he has been drawing comics and his works include *The Story Of Kites* and *The Faint-Hearted Hero*. He has also participated in the production of *One Riddle For One Story*. His comics entitled *Origins of Chinese Festivals* published by Asiapac Books has been widely acclaimed.

About the Translator

Wu Jingyu, born in 1928, studied journalism at Yenching University from 1944 to 1948. She studied at the Beijing Foreign Language School in 1950, where translators and interpreters were trained. She began her teaching career in 1954 and has taught Chinese, Chinese Literature, English and European Literature at various American, Canadian and Chinese universities. She is now Professor of English, specialising in teaching English as a second language at the Beijing Second Foreign Language Institute.

Contents

PROLOGUE

Kunshan[1] County in Jiangsu Province derived its name from a mountain in its boundaries, which, in turn, was thus named because many distinguished people in China's history had lived near it.

During the Jin Dynasty, two brothers, Lu Ji and Lu Yun, lived in Kunshan. As both were exceptionally talented, people referred to them as "precious jade".

According to ancient Chinese legend, jade was produced in Kunlun[2] Mountain, which was also called Kunshan. Therefore, the mountain where the Lu family lived was called Kunshan.

[1] 昆山 [2] 昆仑

2

In 1617, during the rule of Emperor Shenzong of the Ming Dynasty, the nation was enjoying economic properity, but there were political problems. Signs of civil unrest were starting to emerge.

That year a male baby was born to a family named Zhu living at the foot of Kunshan Mountain.

What shall we call him?

Ours is a family with a long line of scholars. I hope he, too, will concentrate on his studies.

Let's call him Yongchun.[1]

[1] 用纯

3

When he was 20, he passed the imperial examination at the county level and became a *xiucai*.[1]

Yongchun grew up to be an avid student.

The Master says...

My son has lived up to my expectations.

At that time, the nation was in chaos. Wu Sankui, a Ming general, collaborated with the Manchus in the north and helped their troops break through government defence at the Great Wall. The Ming Dynasty was thus overthrown and the Qing Dynasty established.

[1] 秀才

4

Yongchun, you should secure an official position just as I have.

That is out of the question! I am a Ming subject and share the same surname with its royal family. I've decided to live in seclusion.

Thus Yongchun adopted an assumed name, Bolu,[1] to express his determination to live in poverty in a hut surrounded by cypress trees.

He lived a hermit's life studying the works by rationalist masters Cheng Hao, Cheng Yi and Zhu Xi, and wrote essays collected in *Kui Ne Ji*[2] and notes on *Daxue*[3] *(The Great Learning)* and *Zhongyong*[4] *(The Doctrine of the Mean)*.

[1] 柏庐 [2] 愧讷集 [3] 大学 [4] 中庸

5

6

7

It tells how one should conduct himself in society, manage his household and cultivate his own character.

I'm sure we'll benefit greatly by following its code.

More and more people took the maxims as their guide. Soon, the booklet which was given the title *Maxims by Zhu Zi* became known all over the country.

During the rule of Emperor Kangxi, China enjoyed prosperity. Zhu Bolu kept his vow to live in seclusion till the end of his life. When he died in 1688, the emperor bestowed on him the title of Xiao Ding[1] to honour him as a man of steadfastness and filial devotion.

The 506-word *Maxims by Zhu Zi* has been popular in China for more than three hundred years. It has been used as guidance in life not only by descendants of the Zhu family but also by the whole nation.

¹ 孝定

MAXIMS
BY
ZHU ZI

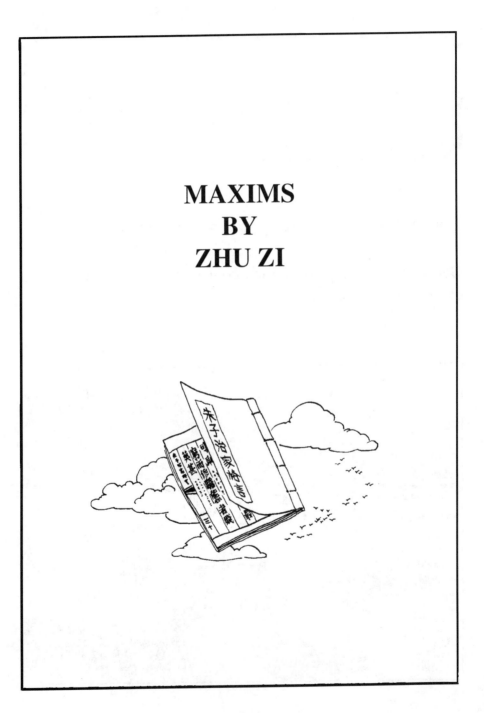

黎 明 即 起 ， 洒 扫 庭 除 ， 要 内 外 整 洁 ；
lí míng jí qǐ   sǎ sǎo tíng chú   yào nèi wài zhěng jié

天刚刚亮就起身，清扫庭院。房里房外都要整齐洁净。

Get up at dawn and sweep the courtyard, so that the house is clean inside and outside.

黎明即起，洒扫庭除，要内外整洁；

The first rays of dawn are like gold.

Is Mr. Zhang in?

I haven't seen you for a long time.

My room is always clean and tidy; so the sudden arrival of a visitor does not make me feel uneasy.

Everything on earth starts its daily operation when the sun rises. People should also get out of bed, clean their rooms and sweep the courtyard. They will feel fresh and clean when they greet the new day.

既 昏 便 息 ， 关 锁 门 户 ， 必 亲 自 检 点 。
jì hūn biàn xī　　guān suǒ mén hù　　bì qīn zì jiǎn diǎn

到黄昏就歇息；关锁门窗，务必亲自检查一番，千万不可大意。

Rest early at night. Check personally that the doors and windows are properly shut.

既昏便息，关锁门户，必亲自检点。

16

17

一粥一饭， 当思来处不易；
yì zhōu yí fàn　　dāng sī lái chù bú yì

半丝半缕， 恒念物力维艰。
bàn sī bàn lǚ　　héng niàn wù lì wéi jiān

一碗粥一粒饭都应想想其来之不易。半根丝半缕纱应常想造物之艰难。

When you eat, remember that food is the product of hard work. When you put on clothes, keep in mind that materials do not come by easily.

一粥一饭，当思来处不易；

半丝半缕，恒念物力维艰。

The things we use to sustain our lives are hard-earned.

I see. Each grain of rice and each inch of cloth are the fruit of hard work.

So we must cherish all that we have.

I won't drop rice on the table anymore.

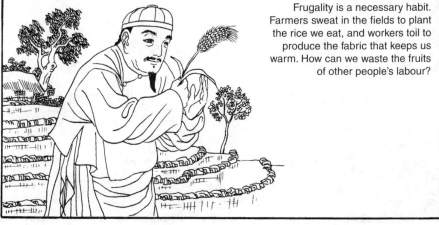

Frugality is a necessary habit. Farmers sweat in the fields to plant the rice we eat, and workers toil to produce the fabric that keeps us warm. How can we waste the fruits of other people's labour?

宜 未 雨 而 绸 缪 ， 毋 临 渴 而 掘 井 。
yí wèi yǔ ér chóu móu wú lín kě ér júe jǐng

最好趁着天没下雨，先修缮房屋门窗，凡事先准备，不要到口渴的时候才去挖井，缓不救急。

One should repair the house before it rains and not start digging a well when he already feels thirsty.

宜未雨而綢繆，毋臨渴而掘井。

24

25

There's no harm in being prepared. Let me help you.

Thanks!

All the leaks have been mended.

Let it rain! Let it rain!

Be sure to mend your roof before the rain comes. Be prepared for exigencies. If you wait till you feel thirsty and then start digging a well, it would be too late.

自 奉 必 须 俭 约 ， 宴 客 切 夕
zì fèng bì xù jiǎn yuè   yàn kè qiè v

自己过日子一定要从俭节省，宴请宾客一定不要小家子气。

Be thrifty in satisfying your own needs, but generous in hosting a reception.

自奉必须俭约，宴客切勿留连。

器 具 质 而 洁 ， 瓦 缶 胜 金 玉 ；
qì jù zhì ér jié　　wǎ fǒu shèng jīn yù

器具要质朴洁净，瓦罐陶器虽然不值钱，但比金杯玉盏更适用。

Utensils used in the house should be plain and clean. Earthenware is better than those made of jade and gold.

器具质而洁，瓦缶胜金玉；

饮 食 约 而 精 ， 园 蔬 愈 珍 馐 。
yǐn shí yuè ér jīng　　yuán shū yù zhēn xiū

饮食要少而精，蔬菜粗粮胜过山珍海味。

Meals need not be sumptuous; finely prepared, simple vegetables can be better than rare delicacies.

37

38

勿 营 华 屋 ， 勿 谋 良 田 。
wù yíng huá wū　　wù móu liáng tián

不要营造华丽的屋子，不要贪取肥沃的田地。

Do not construct extravagant mansions; do not try to gain fertile farmland.

勿营华屋，勿谋良田。

¹One mou is equivalent to 666.7 square metres.

三　姑　六　婆　，　实　淫　盗　之　媒　；
sān　gū　liù　pó　　shí　yín　dào　zhī　méi

婢　美　妾　娇　，　非　闺　房　之　福　。
bì　měi　qiè　jiāo　　fēi　guī　fáng　zhī　fú

三姑（尼姑、道姑、卦姑）六婆（做人口买卖的牙婆、媒婆、巫婆、虔婆、药婆、接生婆），实在是诲淫诲盗之媒孽；娇美的妻妾和丫环，并非是家门的福气。

Matchmakers and sorceresses are agents of vice. Pretty maids and a charming wife need not be a blessing.

三姑六婆，实淫盗之媒；

婢美妾娇，非闺房之福。

44

45

童 仆 勿 用 俊 美 ， 妻 妾 切 忌 艳 妆 。
tóng pú wù yòng jùn měi　　qī qèi qiè jì yàn zhāng

不要找俊俏美丽的仆人，不要让妻妾浓妆艳抹。

Do not judge by physical appearance when hiring servants. It is well with you even if your wife and maids look plain without make-up.

47

童仆勿用俊美，妻妾切忌艳妆。

48

49

祖 宗 虽 远 ， 祭 祀 不 可 不 诚 ；
zǔ zōng suī yuǎn   jì sì bù kě bù chéng

子 孙 虽 愚 ， 经 书 不 可 不 读 。
zǐ sūn suī yú   jīng shū bù kě bù dū

祭拜祖宗，虽然隔了好多代，但心里不可不虔诚。
子孙读书，即使生性愚笨，但四书五经不能不读。

Even if ancestors are far removed from us, we should offer sacrifices with reverence. Even if your children are slow-witted, you should still instruct them in the Confucian classics.

祖宗虽远，祭祀不可不诚；

子孙虽愚，经书不可不读。

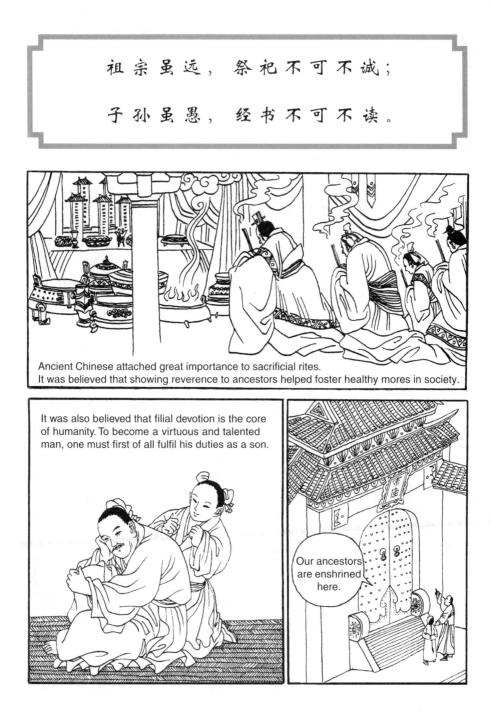

Ancient Chinese attached great importance to sacrificial rites.
It was believed that showing reverence to ancestors helped foster healthy mores in society.

It was also believed that filial devotion is the core of humanity. To become a virtuous and talented man, one must first of all fulfil his duties as a son.

Our ancestors are enshrined here.

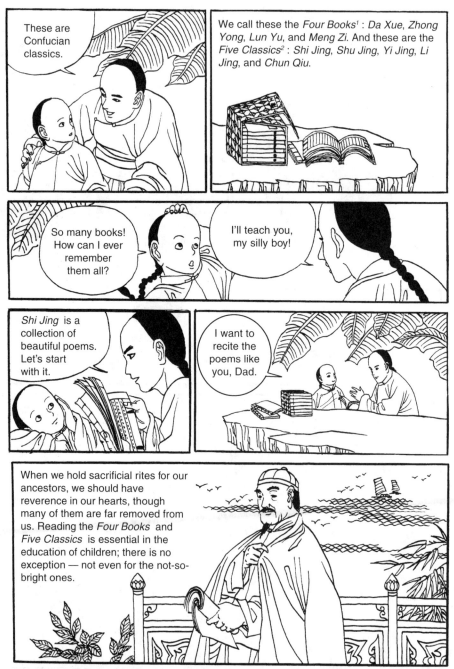

These are Confucian classics.

We call these the *Four Books*[1] : *Da Xue*, *Zhong Yong*, *Lun Yu*, and *Meng Zi*. And these are the *Five Classics*[2] : *Shi Jing*, *Shu Jing*, *Yi Jing*, *Li Jing*, and *Chun Qiu*.

So many books! How can I ever remember them all?

I'll teach you, my silly boy!

Shi Jing is a collection of beautiful poems. Let's start with it.

I want to recite the poems like you, Dad.

When we hold sacrificial rites for our ancestors, we should have reverence in our hearts, though many of them are far removed from us. Reading the *Four Books* and *Five Classics* is essential in the education of children; there is no exception — not even for the not-so-bright ones.

[1] *The Great Learning, The Doctrine of the Mean, The Analects of Confucius*, and *Mencius* respectively (大学，中庸，论语，孟子).
[2] *The Book of Songs, The Book of History, The Book of Changes, The Book of Rites*, and *The Spring & Autumn Annals* respectively (诗经，书经，易经，礼经，春秋).

居 身 务 期 俭 朴 ， 教 子 要 有 义 方 ；
jū shēn wù qī jiǎn pǔ   jiào zǐ yào yǒu yì fāng

勤俭持家，生活朴实应当以身作则，教育子女一定要讲究
方法。

Strive to lead a simple and thrifty life; through such example
your children will learn the principles of living.

居身務期儉樸，教子要有義方；

莫 贪 意 外 之 财 ， 莫 饮 过 量 之 酒 。
mò tān yì wài zhī cái   mò yǐn guò liàng zhī jiǔ

不要贪图意外钱财，不要喝过量的酒。

Do not be tempted by unexpected gains; do not drink more than your capacity.

莫贪意外之财，莫饮过量之酒。

61

与 肩 挑 贸 易 ， 毋 占 便 宜；
yǔ jiān tiāo mào yì   wú zhàn pián yi

遇到小本经营的小贩，不要占便宜;

When dealing with pedlars, do not try to take advantage of them.

与肩挑贸易，毋占便宜；

65

Er...r...r, all right. You can have it.

I also need sewing needles. May I have these, too?

Sister, I'm just a petty trader...

I'll pay for the things she took; I know it's not easy for you to make a living.

Humph, so stingy!

Thank you very much!

Itinerant pedlars live a hard life. They do business with little capital and earn meagre profits. How can anyone have the heart to take advantage of them?

见 穷 苦 亲 邻 ， 须 加 温 恤 。
jiàn qíong kǔ qīn lín　　xū jiā wēn xù

对穷苦的亲戚邻居要格外温存抚恤。

Show sympathy and solicitude to your relatives or neighbours who are in adverse circumstances.

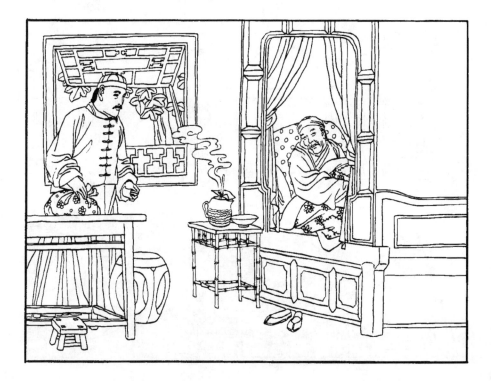

见穷苦亲邻，须加温恤。

70

刻 薄 成 家 ， 理 无 久 享 ；
kè bó chéng jiā   lǐ wú jiǔ xiǎng

伦 常 乖 舛 ， 立 见 消 亡 。
lún cháng guāi chuǎn   lì jiàn xiāo wáng

靠刻薄的手段建立的家业，一定不能长久，做违背伦理道
德的事，家业很快就会衰败消亡。

Fortune amassed by unjust means cannot be enjoyed for long;
violating moral principles will bring about destruction.

71

刻薄成家，理无久享；

伦常乖舛，立见消亡。

72

73

兄 弟 叔 侄 ， 需 分 多 润 寡 ；
xiōng dì shū zhí xū fēn duō rùn guǎ

兄弟叔侄至亲骨肉，财产多的要拿些钱出来接济贫穷的。

Among brothers and close relations, the more affluent should help the needy.

78

长 幼 内 外 ， 宜 法 肃 辞 严 。
zhǎng yòu nèi wài　　yí　fǎ　sù　cí　yán

长幼尊卑，要有严格的规矩；男女之间，内外有别。

In a family, parents and children, husband and wife, the older and younger should each do their duty. They should all abide strictly by the rules of behaviour and use appropriate language.

长幼内外，宜法肃辞严。

If parents and children, husband and wife, older and younger brothers keep their own places and do their duties, the family will be harmonious and in good order.

The traditional idea about family is that the man deals with the outside world while the wife takes care of household matters.

The stability of society is maintained on the basis of harmonious families.

听 妇 言 ， 乖 骨 肉 ， 岂 是 丈 夫 ；
tīng fù yán　　guāi gǔ ròu　　qǐ shì zhàng fū

听信妇人的胡说，乖离骨肉之情，这哪里是大丈夫的行为。

A father who believes the slanderous talk of a woman and turns against his own flesh and blood cannot be called a true man.

听 妇 言 ， 乖 骨 肉 ， 岂 是 丈 夫 ；

84

85

Could she be lying to me?

It's all my fault that she behaves badly.

Now she steals and lies as well.

Don't get upset, dear.

Take no notice of that ill-behaving girl.

A man who estranges himself from his own flesh and blood because he believes a woman's slanderous talk is not an upright man.

重赀财 ， 薄父母 ， 不成人子 。
zhòng zī cái   bó fù mǔ   bù chéng rén zǐ

只看重资产钱财，刻薄对待父母，不能算作人的子女。

A man who values money more than his parents is a bad son.

重赀财，薄父母，不成人子。

嫁 女 择 佳 婿 ， 毋 索 重 聘 ；
jià nǚ zé jiā xù　　wú suǒ zhòng pìn

嫁闺女，要选择品质好的女婿，不要一味索取过多的聘礼。

When marrying off a daughter, choose a man of good qualities. It is wrong to demand lavish betrothal gifts.

嫁女择佳婿，毋索重聘；

93

I've often heard people say that wealth and rank are as transient as a fleeting cloud, but a good spouse ensures happiness of a lifetime.

My dear daughter, the Li family has neither money nor rank. If you choose him, you'll be plunging into the pit of hell.

Mother, I've always thought highly of the young Mr. Li. I think I'll accept the hairpin.

What a well-matched couple!

If a father chooses a husband for his daughter according to the value of the betrothal gifts he offers, it is doubtful whether the daughter's happiness can be secured. Her happiness should be entrusted to a man of good moral character and talents.

94

娶　媳　求　淑　女　，　勿　计　厚　奁　。
qǔ　xí　qiú　shū　nǚ　　　wù　jì　hòu　lián

娶媳妇要寻求贤淑女子，不要计较妆奁的厚薄。

When choosing a wife for a son, find a girl who is virtuous and genial, not one whose family offers a generous dowry.

娶媳求淑女，勿计厚奁。

96

97

98

见 富 贵 而 生 谄 容 者 ， 最 可 耻 ；
jiàn fù guì ér shēng chǎn róng zhě　　zuì kě chǐ

见到有钱有势的人就露出一副媚态的人，最为可耻。

People who fawn over the rich and powerful are most despicable.

99

見富貵而生諂容者，最可耻；

遇 贫 穷 而 作 骄 态 者 ， 贱 莫 甚 。
yù pín qíong ér zuò jiāo tài zhě   jiàn mò shèn

遇到贫寒穷困的人就显出骄人的姿态，这是最为下贱的了。

People who behave arrogantly towards the poor are themselves the most contemptible.

遇贫穷而作骄态者，贱莫甚。

105

居 家 戒 争 讼 ， 讼 则 终 凶 ；
jū jiā jiè zhēng sòng　　sòng zé zhōngxiōng

居家度日切忌和别人争争吵吵，打官司，因为打起官司来
终是凶多吉少。

Avoid lawsuit to settle domestic disputes; litigation often has
bad results.

居家戒争讼，讼则终凶；

处 世 戒 多 言 ， 言 多 必 失 。
chǔ shì jiè duō yán   yán duō bì shī

为人处世不要多嘴多舌，话多了必然会惹祸生事。

When with others, do not talk too much. One who talks too much is prone to say the wrong thing.

处世戒多言，言多必失。

113

¹ Salted duck eggs are made by coating eggs with salt and sealing them with a layer of earth for 20 days or more.

勿 恃 势 力 而 凌 逼 孤 寡 ，
wù shì shì lì ér líng bī gū guǎ

不要依仗权势欺凌逼迫孤儿寡妇。

Do not use one's power to oppress the orphaned and widowed.

115

勿恃势力而凌逼孤寡，

116

117

118

毋 贪 口 腹 而 恣 杀 牲 禽 。
wú tān kǒu fù ér zì shā shēng qín

不要为贪图口腹的快乐而任意杀害鸟兽。

One should not recklessly kill livestock to indulge his appetite.

120

毋贪口腹而恣杀牲禽。

The ox is crying.

I'm afraid roast beef will give me stomachache.

I've suddenly lost my appetite.

Do not kill livestock to satisfy your desire for good food. Animals prey to sustain themselves. Men should not behave as fiercely as beasts.

乖 僻 自 是 ， 悔 误 必 多 ；
guāi pì zì shì   huǐ wù bì duō

一个人性情乖僻，自以为是，将来后悔和做错的事必然就多。

Eccentricity and conceit often misguide a person and result in regret.

The young man eventually returned home.

You've come back. How was business?

Everything's lost. If only I had...

You never listened to my advice.

Well, at least you're back safe and sound.

I was wrong.

Being self-opinionated and turning a deaf ear to the advice of others often result in mistakes and regrets.

颓隳自甘 ， 家道难成 。
tuí huī zì gān   jiā dào nán chéng

一个人颓靡懒惰，自甘沦落，将来的家业一定难以建立。

One who is spiritless and lazy can achieve nothing.

颓隳自甘，家道难成。

134

狎 昵 恶 少 ， 久 必 受 其 累 ；
xiá nì è shào   jiǔ bì shòu qí lěi

接近轻佻恶少年，日久必然受他的连累。

Keeping company with a profligate young man, one will ultimately suffer because of him.

狎昵惡少，久必受其累；

136

138

屈 志 老 成 ， 急 则 可 相 依 。
qū zhì lǎo chéng   jí zé kě xiāng yī

结交稳重老成的人虽然不太惬意，但急难之时可有依靠。

Men who are experienced, prudent and modest can be depended on during an emergency.

屈志老成，急则可相依。

141

144

轻 听 发 言 ， 安 知 非 人 之 谮 诉 ？
qīng tīng fā yán　　ān zhī fēi rén zhī zèn sù

当 忍 耐 三 思 ；
dāng rěn nài sān sī

轻信别人的话，怎知不是别人的造谣中伤，应当耐住性子
三思。

When hearing an accusation, do not readily believe it. Keep your cool and think carefully, for the charge may be false.

轻听发言，安知非人之谮诉？

当忍耐三思；

148

因 事 相 争 ， 焉 知 非 我 之 不 是 ？
yīn shì xiāng zhēng   yān zhī fēi wǒ zhī bú shì

需 平 心 暗 想 。
xū píng xīn àn xiǎng

因一时之事口角相争，怎知不是自己的不对？须平心静气地自省。

When engaged in an argument, one should calmly ask himself whether he is at fault.

因事相争，焉知非我之不是？
需平心暗想。

152

154

施惠无念 ， 受恩莫忘 。
shī huì wú niàn shòu ēn mò wàng

施人恩惠不要挂在心上，受人恩惠不要忘记报答。

Do not keep in mind a favour you have bestowed on someone else, but do not forget to repay a favour you have received.

施惠无念，受恩莫忘。

157

158

凡 事 当 留 余 地 ， 得 意 不 宜 再 往 。
fán shì dāng liú yú dì　　dé yì bù yí zài wǎng

凡事应当留有余地，见好就收不要贪心再去寻求。

Whatever you do, always allow some leeway for unforeseen circumstances. When you are successful in one endeavour, do not aspire to have the success repeated.

凡事当留余地，得意不宜再往。

161

162

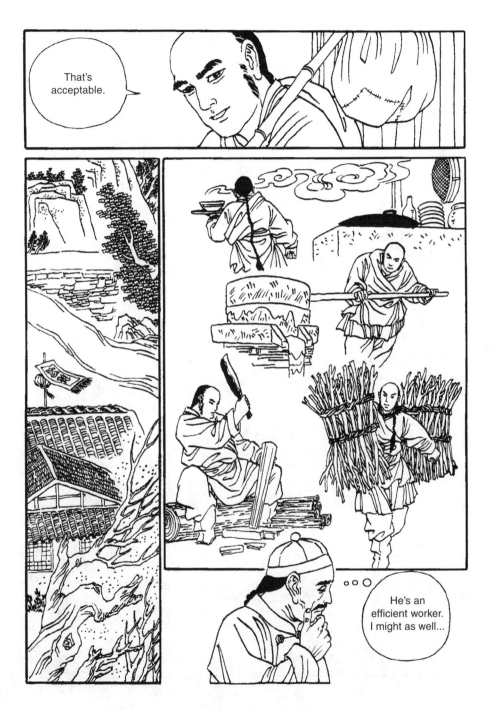

164

人 有 喜 庆 ， 不 可 生 妒 嫉 心 ；
rén yǒu xǐ qìng　　bù kě shēng dù jì xīn

人 有 祸 患 ， 不 可 生 喜 幸 心 。
rén yǒu huò huàn　　bù kě shēng xǐ xìn xīn

他人有喜庆之事，不要生妒嫉之心；他人有祸患，不要暗暗幸灾乐祸。

Do not be envious of other people's happiness. Do not take pleasure in other people's misfortune.

人有喜庆，不可生妒嫉心；

人有祸患，不可生喜幸心。

167

169

善 欲 人 见 ， 不 是 真 善 ；
shàn yù rén jiàn　　bú shì zhēn shàn

恶 恐 人 知 ， 便 是 大 恶 。
è kǒng rén zhī　　biàn shì dà è

做好事想让人知道，不是真正的做好事。
做了坏事又生怕别人知道，这才是大恶。

One who gives publicity to his good deeds is not genuinely
doing good. One who tries to conceal his wrongdoing has
committed great evil indeed.

善欲人見，不是真善；

惡恐人知，便是大惡。

171

173

见 色 而 起 淫 心 ， 报 在 妻 女 ；
jiàn sè ér qǐ yín xīn   bào zài qī nǚ

见美色而动淫邪之心，报应会落到妻子女儿身上。

If a man has lascivious ideas when he sees a beautiful woman, his punishment will be visited upon his wife and daughter.

Back home.

My daughter has gone to do some shopping. She's been out a long time.

Why hasn't she come back?

There she is.

Your dad has been waiting for you, Young Mistress.

Some rascals pestered Young Mistress. We had a hard time getting rid of them.

Despicable scoundrels! Beware of them in future.

If you have indecent ideas when you see a beautiful woman, or even make a pass at her, other men may do the same to your wife or daughter. Therefore, do not do unto others what you would not wish to happen to your own family.

178

匿 怨 而 用 暗 箭 ， 祸 延 子 孙 。
nì yuàn ér yòng àn jiàn　huò yán zǐ sūn'

藏匿怨恨而用暗箭伤人，祸患会蔓延给子孙。

If a man harbours a grudge and vent his spite by underhand means, he is inviting misfortune upon his descendants.

匿怨而用暗箭，禍延子孫。

181

家 门 和 顺 ， 虽 饔 飧 不 继 ， 亦 有 余 欢 ；
jiā mén hé shùn　　suī yōng sūn bú jì　　yì yǒu yú huān

一家人和睦相处，即使遇到吃了上顿没有下顿的时候，也有天伦之乐。

When a family lives together in harmony and peace, even if they are poor and can hardly make ends meet, they will enjoy plenty of happiness.

184

国 课 早 完 ， 即 囊 橐 无 余 ， 自 得 至 乐 。
guō kè zǎo wán　　jí náng tuó wú yú　　zì dé zhì lè

早日交完官粮和国税，即使囊中没有剩余的钱粮，也能心安理得。

When a man has paid his taxes and levies, though his pockets are empty, he feels vastly gratified.

国课早完，即囊橐无余，自得至乐。

读 书 志 在 圣 贤 ，
dú shū zhì zài shèng xián

习读经书是希望成为圣贤。

A man ought to study with the aspiration to become a man of virtue.

读书志在圣贤，

为 官 心 存 君 国 。
wéi guān xīn cún jūn guó

做官时心里要装着君主和国家。

A man serving as an official ought to have the interests of the emperor and the nation at heart.

为官心存君国。

197

A few days later.

Look, isn't that the new magistrate? He's come to inspect the countryside.

He's really a good official.

He does have the interest of the state at heart.

The job of an official is to serve the people. He must bear in mind the interest of the state and the people, and be concerned about the weal and woe of the masses.

守 分 安 命 ， 顺 时 听 天 。
shǒu fèn ān mìng   shùn shí tīng tiān

为 人 若 此 ， 庶 乎 近 焉 ！
wéi rén ruò cǐ   shù hū jìn yán

奉守本分，接受命运的安排，顺应时势，听从老天的旨意。
为人处世能象这样，就差不多接近理想的境界了。

One must be faithful in his duty and contented in his lot. He must follow the proper course of the time and comply with the mandate of heaven. One who lives in this way has about attained the state of perfection.

守分安命，顺时听天。

为人若此，庶乎近焉！

APPENDIXES

Classical Text

Chinese Paraphrase

English Translation

Classical Text

51 祖 宗 虽 远 ， 祭 祀 不 可 不 诚 ；
zǔ zōng suī yuǎn jì sì bù kě bù chéng

子 孙 虽 愚 ， 经 书 不 可 不 读 。
zǐ sūn suī yú jīng shū bù kě bù dū

55 居 身 务 期 俭 朴 ， 教 子 要 有 义 方 ；
jū shēn wù qī jiǎn pǔ jiào zǐ yào yǒu yì fāng

59 莫 贪 意 外 之 财 ， 莫 饮 过 量 之 酒 。
mò tān yì wài zhī cái mò yǐn guò liàng zhī jiǔ

63 与 肩 挑 贸 易 ， 毋 占 便 宜 ；
yǔ jiān tiāo mào yì wú zhàn pián yi

67 见 穷 苦 亲 邻 ， 须 加 温 恤 。
jiàn qíong kǔ qīn lín xū jiā wēn xù

71 刻 薄 成 家 ， 理 无 久 享 ；
kè bó chéng jiā lǐ wú jiǔ xiǎng

伦 常 乖 舛 ， 立 见 消 亡 。
lún cháng guāi chuǎn lì jiàn xiāo wáng

75 兄 弟 叔 侄 ， 需 分 多 润 寡 ；
xiōng dì shū zhí xū fēn duō rùn guǎ

79 长 幼 内 外 ， 宜 法 肃 辞 严 。
zhǎng yòu nèi wài yí fǎ sù cí yán

83 听 妇 言 ， 乖 骨 肉 ， 岂 是 丈 夫 ；
tīng fù yán guāi gǔ ròu qǐ shì zhàng fū

87 重 赀 财 ， 薄 父 母 ， 不 成 人 子 。
zhòng zī cái bó fù mǔ bù chéng rén zǐ

91 嫁 女 择 佳 婿 ， 毋 索 重 聘 ；
jià nǚ zé jiā xù wú suǒ zhòng pìn

95 娶 媳 求 淑 女 ， 勿 计 厚 奁 。
qǔ xí qiú shū nǚ wù jì hòu lián

99........ 见 富 贵 而 生 谄 容 者 ， 最 可 耻 ；
jiàn fù guì ér shēng chǎn róng zhě zuì kě chǐ

103...... 遇 贫 穷 而 作 骄 态 者 ， 贱 莫 甚 。
yù pín qióng ér zuò jiāo tài zhě jiàn mò shèn

107...... 居 家 戒 争 讼 ， 讼 则 终 凶 ；
jū jiā jiè zhēng sòng sòng zé zhōng xiōng

111...... 处 世 戒 多 言 ， 言 多 必 失 。
chǔ shì jiè duō yán yán duō bì shī

115...... 勿 恃 势 力 而 凌 逼 孤 寡 ，
wù shì shì lì ér líng bī gū guǎ

120...... 毋 贪 口 腹 而 恣 杀 牲 禽 。
wú tān kǒu fù ér zì shā shēng qín

125...... 乖 僻 自 是 ， 悔 误 必 多 ；
guāi pì zì shì huǐ wù bì duō

130...... 颓 隳 自 甘 ， 家 道 难 成 。
tuí huī zì gān jiā dào nán chéng

135...... 狎 昵 恶 少 ， 久 必 受 其 累 ；
xiá nì è shào jiǔ bì shòu qí lěi

140...... 屈 志 老 成 ， 急 则 可 相 依 。
qū zhì lǎo chéng jí zé kě xiāng yī

145...... 轻 听 发 言 ， 安 知 非 人 之 谮 诉 ？
qīng tīng fā yán ān zhī fēi rén zhī zèn sù

当 忍 耐 三 思 ；
dāng rěn nài sān sī

150...... 因 事 相 争 ， 焉 知 非 我 之 不 是 ？
yīn shì xiāng zhēng yān zhī fēi wǒ zhī bú shì

需 平 心 暗 想 。
xū píng xīn àn xiǎng

155...... 施 惠 无 念 ， 受 恩 莫 忘 。
shī huì wú niàn shòu ēn mò wàng

160...... 凡 事 当 留 余 地 ， 得 意 不 宜 再 往 。
fán shì dāng liú yú dì dé yì bù yí zài wǎng

165...... 人 有 喜 庆 ， 不 可 生 妒 嫉 心 ；
rén yǒu xǐ qìng bù kě shēng dù jì xīn

人 有 祸 患 ， 不 可 生 喜 幸 心 。
rén yǒu huò huàn bù kě shēng xǐ xìn xīn

170...... 善 欲 人 见 ， 不 是 真 善 ；
shàn yù rén jiàn bú shì zhēn shàn

恶 恐 人 知 ， 便 是 大 恶 。
è kǒng rén zhī biàn shì dà è

175...... 见 色 而 起 淫 心 ， 报 在 妻 女 ；
jiàn sè ér qǐ yín xīn bào zài qī nǚ

179...... 匿 怨 而 用 暗 箭 ， 祸 延 子 孙 。
nì yuàn ér yòng àn jiàn huò yán zǐ sūn'

183...... 家 门 和 顺 ， 虽 饔 飧 不 继 ， 亦 有 余 欢 ；
jiā mén hé shùn suī yōng sūn bú jì yì yǒu yú huān

187...... 国 课 早 完 ， 即 囊 橐 无 余 ， 自 得 至 乐 。
guō kè zǎo wán jí náng tuó wú yú zì dé zhì lè

191...... 读 书 志 在 圣 贤 ，
dú shū zhì zài shèng xián

195...... 为 官 心 存 君 国 。
wéi guān xīn cún jūn guó

199...... 守 分 安 命 ， 顺 时 听 天 。
shǒu fèn ān mìng shùn shí tīng tiān

为 人 若 此 ， 庶 乎 近 焉 ！
wéi rén ruò cǐ shù hū jìn yán

Chinese Paraphrase

天刚刚亮就起身，清扫庭院。房里房外都要整齐洁净。

到黄昏就歇息；关锁门窗，务必亲自检查一番，千万不可大意。

一碗粥一粒饭都应想想其来之不易。半根丝半缕纱应常想造物之艰难。

最好趁着天没下雨，先修缮房屋门窗，凡事先准备，不要到口渴的时候才去挖井，缓不救急。

自己过日子一定要从俭节省，宴请宾客一定不要小家子气。

器具要质朴洁净，瓦罐陶器虽然不值钱，但比金杯玉盏更适用。

饮食要少而精，蔬菜粗粮胜过山珍海味。

不要营造华丽的屋子，不要贪取肥沃的田地。

三姑（尼姑、道姑、卦姑）六婆（做人口买卖的牙婆、媒婆、巫婆、虔婆、药婆、接生婆），实在是诲淫诲盗之媒孽；娇美的妻妾和丫环，并非是家门的福气。

不要找俊俏美丽的仆人，不要让妻妾浓妆艳抹。

祭拜祖宗，虽然隔了好多代，但心里不可不虔诚。

子孙读书，即使生性愚笨，但四书五经不能不读。

勤俭持家，生活朴实应当以身作则，教育子女一定要讲究方法。

不要贪图意外钱财，不要喝过量的酒。

遇到小本经营的小贩，不要占便宜；

对穷苦的亲戚邻居要格外温存抚恤。

靠刻薄的手段建立的家业，一定不能长久，做违背伦理道德的事，家业很快就会衰败消亡。

兄弟叔侄至亲骨肉，财产多的要拿些钱出来接济贫穷的。

长幼尊卑，要有严格的规矩；男女之间，内外有别。

听信妇人的胡说，乖离骨肉之情，这哪里是大丈夫的行为。

只看重资产钱财，刻薄对待父母，不能算作人的子女。

嫁闺女，要选择品质好的女婿，不要一味索取过多的聘礼。

娶媳妇要寻求贤淑女子，不要计较妆奁的厚薄。

见到有钱有势的人就露出一副媚态的人，最为可耻。

遇到贫寒穷困的人就显出骄人的姿态，这是最为下贱的了。

居家度日切忌和别人争争吵吵，打官司，因为打起官司来终是凶多吉少。

为人处世不要多嘴多舌，话多了必然会惹祸生事。

不要依仗权势欺凌逼迫孤儿寡妇。

不要为贪图口腹的快乐而任意杀害鸟兽。

一个人性情乖僻，自以为是，将来后悔和做错的事必然就多；

一个人颓靡懒惰，自甘沦落，将来的家业一定难以建立。

接近轻佻恶少年，日久必然受他的连累；

结交稳重老成的人虽然不太惬意，但急难之时可有依靠。

轻信别人的话，怎知不是别人的造谣中伤，应当耐住性子三思。

因一时之事口角相争，怎知不是自己的不对？须平心静气地自省。

施人恩惠不要挂在心上，受人恩惠不要忘记报答。

凡事应当留有余地，见好就收不要贪心再去寻求。

他人有喜庆之事，不要生妒嫉之心；他人有祸患，不要暗暗幸灾乐祸。

做好事想让人知道，不是真正的做好事。
做了坏事又生怕别人知道，这才是大恶。

见美色而动淫邪之心，报应会落到妻子女儿身上；

藏匿怨恨而用暗箭伤人，祸患会蔓延给子孙。

一家人和睦相处，即使遇到吃了上顿没有下顿的时候，也有天伦之乐。

早日交完官粮和国税，即使囊中没有剩余的钱粮，也能心安理得。

习读经书是希望成为圣贤，

做官时心里要装着君主和国家。

奉守本分，接受命运的安排，顺应时势，听从老天的旨意。
为人处世能象这样，就差不多接近理想的境界了。

English Translation

43...... Matchmakers and sorceresses are agents of vice. Pretty maids and a charming wife need not be a blessing.

47...... Do not judge by physical appearance when hiring servants. It is well with you even if your wife and maids look plain without make-up.

51...... Even if ancestors are far removed from us, we should offer sacrifices with reverence. Even if your children are slow-witted, you should still instruct them in the Confucian classics.

55...... Strive to lead a simple and thrifty life; through such example your children will learn the principles of living.

59...... Do not be tempted by unexpected gains; do not drink more than your capacity.

63...... When dealing with pedlars, do not try to take advantage of them.

67...... Show sympathy and solicitude to your relatives or neighbours who are in adverse circumstances.

71...... Fortune amassed by unjust means cannot be enjoyed for long; violating moral principles will bring about destruction.

75...... Among brothers and close relations, the more affluent should help the needy.

79...... In a family, parents and children, husband and wife, the older and younger should each do their duty. They should all abide strictly by the rules of behaviour and use appropriate language.

83...... A father who believes the slanderous talk of a woman and turns against his own flesh and blood cannot be called a true man.

87...... A man who values money more than his parents is a bad son.

91...... When marrying off a daughter, choose a man of good qualities. It is wrong to demand lavish betrothal gifts.

95...... When choosing a wife for a son, find a girl who is virtuous and genial, not one whose family offers a generous dowry.

99...... People who fawn over the rich and powerful are most despicable.

103......People who behave arrogantly towards the poor are themselves the most contemptible.

107...... Avoid lawsuit to settle domestic disputes; litigation often has bad results.

111...... When with others, do not talk too much. One who talks too much is prone to say the wrong thing.

115...... Do not use one's power to oppress the orphaned and widowed.

120...... One should not recklessly kill livestock to indulge his appetite.

125...... Eccentricity and conceit often misguide a person and result in regret.

130...... One who is spiritless and lazy can achieve nothing.

135...... Keeping company with a profligate young man, one will ultimately suffer because of him.

140...... Men who are experienced, prudent and modest can be depended on during an emergency.

145...... When hearing an accusation, do not readily believe it. Keep your cool and think carefully, for the charge may be false.

150...... When engaged in an argument, one should calmly ask himself whether he is at fault.

155...... Do not keep in mind a favour you have bestowed on someone else, but do not forget to repay a favour you have received.

160...... Whatever you do, always allow some leeway for unforeseen circumstances. When you are successful in one endeavour, do not aspire to have the success repeated.

165...... Do not be envious of other people's happiness. Do not take pleasure in other people's misfortune.

170...... One who gives publicity to his good deeds is not genuinely doing good. One who tries to conceal his wrongdoing has committed great evil indeed.

175...... If a man has lascivious ideas when he sees a beautiful woman, his punishment will be visited upon his wife and daughter.

179...... If a man harbours a grudge and vent his spite by underhand means, he is inviting misfortune upon his descendants.

183...... When a family lives together in harmony and peace, even if they are poor and can hardly make ends meet, they will enjoy plenty of happiness.

187...... When a man has paid his taxes and levies, though his pockets are empty, he feels vastly gratified.

191...... A man ought to study with the aspiration to become a man of virtue.

195...... A man serving as an official ought to have the interests of the emperor and the nation at heart.

199...... One must be faithful in his duty and contented in his lot. He must follow the proper course of the time and comply with the mandate of heaven. One who lives in this way has about attained the state of perfection.

Strategy & Leadership Series by Wang Xuanming

Thirty-six Stratagems: Secret Art of War
Translated by Koh Kok Kiang (cartoons) &
            Liu Yi (text of the stratagems)
    A Chinese military classic which emphasizes deceptive schemes to achieve military objectives. It has attracted the attention of military authorities and general readers alike.

Six Strategies for War: The Practice of Effective Leadership
Translated by Alan Chong
    A powerful book for rulers, administrators and leaders, it covers critical areas in management and warfare including: how to recruit talents and manage the state; how to beat the enemy and build an empire; how to lead wisely; and how to manoeuvre brilliantly.

Gems of Chinese Wisdom: Mastering the Art of Leadership
Translated by Leong Weng Kam
    Wise up with this delightful collection of tales and anecdotes on the wisdom of great men and women in Chinese history, including Confucius, Meng Changjun and Gou Jian.

Three Strategies of Huang Shi Gong: The Art of Government
Translated by Alan Chong
    Reputedly one of man's oldest monograph on military strategy, it unmasks the secrets behind brilliant military manoeuvres, clever deployment and control of subordinates, and effective government.

100 Strategies of War: Brilliant Tactics in Action
Translated by Yeo Ai Hoon
    The book captures the essence of extensive military knowledge and practice, and explores the use of psychology in warfare, the importance of building diplomatic relations with the enemy's neighbours, the use of espionage and reconnaissance, etc.

Latest Titles in
Strategy & Leadership Series

Chinese Business Strategies

The Chinese are known for being shrewd businessmen able to thrive under the toughest market conditions. The secret of their success lies in 10 time-tested principles of Chinese entrepreneurship.

This book offers readers 30 real-life, ancient case studies with comments on their application in the context of modern business.

Sixteen Strategies of Zhuge Liang

Zhuge Liang, the legendary statesman and military commander during the Three Kingdoms Period, is the epitome of wisdom.

Well-grounded in military principles of Sun Zi and other masters before him, he excelled in applying them in state administration and his own innovations, thus winning many spectacular victories with his uncanny anticipation of enemy moves.

ADVENTURES of
WISELY
(Sci-fi comics)
Written by Ni Kuang
Illustrated by Wee Tian Beng

THE RETURN OF THE HERMIT
Join Wisely, the dashing daredevil, as he embarks on a thrilling and perilous adventure. A strange request from a blind man leads Wisely to a deadly encounter with the powerful 25 triads. This culminates in a journey to the notorious bandit hideout, Daselle Island, to uncover a secret that has been left buried for years. Amid danger, Wisely romances with Bai Su, the beautiful daughter of the triad leader, while his gregarious cousin lends some light-hearted moments to this fast-moving suspense thriller with her zany character.

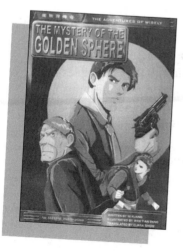

MYSTERY OF THE GOLDEN SPHERE
An unusual request from a group of refugees leads Bai Su to one of the world's most mystic places, Mysteryland, in search of the elusive Golden Sphere. Believing that it contains supernatural powers, both the ousted government and the military junta that took over are also in hot pursuit. Things get really heated up and Bai Su's dashing fiance, Wisely, jumps into action.

SPECIAL OFFER

LIVING 21 SERIES - A powerful new comic series to equip you with timeless principles to be successful and effective in the 21st century.

1. Chinese A.R.T. of Goal Setting
2. Chinese T.A.C.T.I.C. in Negotiation
3. Chinese Art of Leadership

4. Chinese Art of Excellence
5. Chinese Art of Team Building
6. Chinese Art of Commitment

Make your subscription for this new comic series and enjoy **10% discount.**

Original Price for 6 volumes: **S$64.89** (*inclusive of* GST)

Special price for subscription of 6 volumes: **S$58.40** (*inclusive of* GST)

I wish to subscribe for _____ sets of *LIVING 21 SERIES* at the nett price of S$58.40 per set.

Enclosed is my postal order/money order/cheque/ for S$_____ (No.: _____)

Name (Mr/Mrs/Ms) _____ Tel _____

Address _____

_____ Fax _____

Please charge the amount of S$ _____ to my VISA/MASTER CARD account (only Visa/Master Card accepted)

Card No. _____ Card Expiry Date _____

Card Holder's Name (Mr/Mrs/Ms) _____ Signature _____

C⊕ RETURN OF THE ⊕S ONDOR HEROES

神雕俠侶

Subscription Form

Bestselling martial-art comics by Louis Cha
Illustrated by Wee Tian Beng

Per Issue
Usual: S$8.76
Now: S$7.70
(local order)

Now in 18 volumes, published bimonthly. Subscribe now and enjoy special discounts.

I wish to subscribe for *Return of the Condor Heroes Series* from Volume ___ to Volume ___.

❑ Singapore Order: Nett price of S$7.70 per volume (free postage)

❑ Overseas Order: Nett price of S$10.20 per volume (inclusive of postage by surface mail)

Enclosed is my postal order/money order/cheque/ for S$_____ (No.: _____)

Name (Mr/Mrs/Ms) _____ Tel _____

Address _____

_____ Fax _____

Please charge the amount of S$ _____ to my VISA/MASTER CARD account (only

Visa/Master Card accepted)

Card No. _____ Card Expiry Date _____

Card Holder's Name (Mr/Mrs/Ms) _____ Signature _____

Send to: ASIAPAC BOOKS PTE LTD 996 Bendemeer Road #06-08/09 Kallang Basin
Industrial Estate Singapore 339944 Tel: (65)3928455 Fax: (65)3926455
**Note: Prices subject to change without prior notice. Each issue to be mailed to you upon
publication — one volume every two months.**

Mike Chen

陳至真　　1998

≪亚太漫画系列≫

朱子治家格言

编写：陈蝶心

绘画：傅春江

翻译：吴敬瑜

亚太图书有限公司出版